TO YOU,

Grandmother,

from

———————————

"A
GRANDMOTHER
IS LOVE."

ISBN 1-56218-080-0

WITH LOVE TO A
Very Special
Grandmother

"WHAT
IS A
GRANDMOTHER?"

She's that
special someone
who's as dear
as she can be—
Always doing
thoughtful things
to please
her family...

She's kindness
and encouragement,
and patience
    with a smile,
She's understanding
    sympathy
and sweetness
    all the while...

A
GRANDMOTHER
is wisdom,
for she's learned
    along life's way
How to cope
with all the problems
    that can
    come up in a day...

How to make
a sad heart happy,
how to make
the smiles appear—
A grandmother
is thoughtfulness
and helpfulness
and cheer.

She's proud
of our accomplishments,
she thinks
our faults are slight—
She's such
a welcome comfort
when things
just aren't
going right.

She's offerings
of timely thoughts
and tender,
loving care,
And a wealth
of treasured
teachings
that she's always
quick
to share.

A
GRANDMOTHER
is love,
because she gives
her love away
In the very best
example
of a good life
lived
each day.

She's someone
who is
there for us,
no matter
what we do,
Someone
we can turn to
for some warmth
and
friendship,
too.

She's someone
who is patient,
gentle,
thoughtful,
helpful, kind —
I guess you'd say
a grandmother
is life's
nicest things
combined!

When
thoughts go back
across the years,
as now
and then they do,
It seems
so many
memories
are special 'cause
of you...

Because
of your sweet,
giving ways,
your kindness
and good cheer—
Because,
GRANDMOTHER,
you'll always be
so very,
very dear.